THE *Mike Murdock* COLLECTOR'S EDITION

THE
WISDOM
COMMENTARY 1

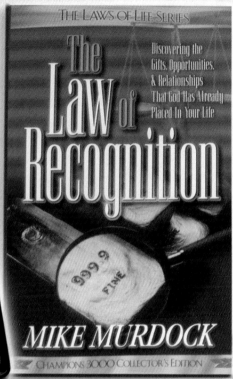

Financial Success.

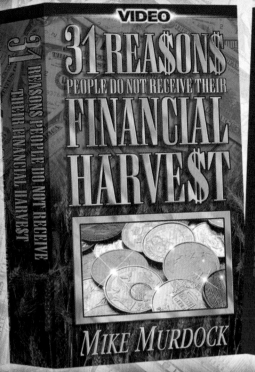

VIDEO
31 REAON
PEOPLE DO NOT RECEIVE THEIR
FINANCIAL HARVE$T
MIKE MURDOCK

7 KEYS to 1000 TIMES MORE

VIDEO
7 KEYS to 1000 TIMES MORE

The Lord God Of Your Fathers
Make You A Thousand Times
So Many More As You Are,
And Bless You, As He Hath
Promised You!
Deuteronomy 1:11

MIKE MURDOCK

▸ **8 Scriptural Reasons You Should Pursue Financial Prosperity**

▸ **The Secret Prayer Key You Need When Making A Financial Request To God**

▸ **The Weapon Of Expectation And The 5 Miracles It Unlocks**

▸ **How To Discern Those Who Qualify To Receive Your Financial Assistance**

▸ **How To Predict The Miracle Moment God Will Schedule Your Financial Breakthrough**

▸ **Habits Of Uncommon Achievers**

▸ **The Greatest Success Law I Ever Discovered**

▸ **How To Discern Your Place Of Assignment, The Only Place Financial Provision Is Guaranteed**

▸ **3 Secret Keys In Solving Problems For Others**

The Wisdom Center

Video Pak AMVIDEO | **$30**
Buy 1-Get 1 Free
(A $60 Value!)

Wisdom Is The Principal Thing

Add 10% For S/H

THE WISDOM CENTER
P.O. Box 99, Denton, Texas 76202

1-888-WISDOM1
(1-888-947-3661)

Website:
WWW.THEWISDOMCENTER.TV

C

Songs From The Secret Place!

The Music Ministry of MIKE MURDOCK

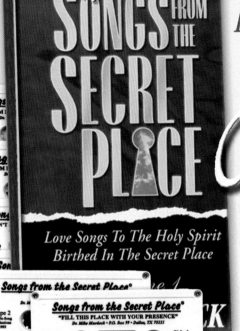

Love Songs To The Holy Spirit Birthed In The Secret Place

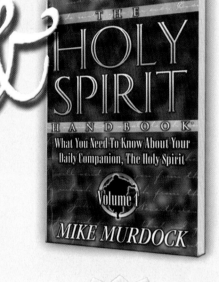

THE HOLY SPIRIT HANDBOOK
What You Need To Know About Your Daily Companion, The Holy Spirit

Volume 1

MIKE MURDOCK

Songs...

1. A Holy Place
2. Anything You Want
3. Everything Comes From You
4. Fill This Place With Your Presence
5. First Thing Every Morning
6. Holy Spirit, I Want To Hear You
7. Holy Spirit, Move Again
8. Holy Spirit, You Are Enough
9. I Don't Know What I Would Do Without You
10. I Let Go (Of Anything That Stops Me)
11. I'll Just Fall On You
12. I Love You, Holy Spirit
13. I'm Building My Life Around You
14. I'm Giving Myself To You
15. I'm In Love! I'm In Love!
16. I Need Water (Holy Spirit, You're My Well)
17. In The Secret Place
18. In Your Presence, I'm Always Changed
19. In Your Presence (Miracles Are Born)
20. I've Got To Live In Your Presence
21. I Want To Hear Your Voice
22. I Will Do Things Your Way
23. Just One Day At A Time
24. Meet Me In The Secret Place
25. More Than Ever Before
26. Nobody Else Does What You Do
27. No No Walls!
28. Nothing Else Matters Anymore (Since I've Been In The Presence Of You Lord)
29. Nowhere Else
30. Once Again You've Answered
31. Only A Fool Would Try (To Live Without You)
32. Take Me Now
33. Teach Me How To Please You
34. There's No Place I'd Rather Be
35. Thy Word Is All That Matters
36. When I Get In Your Presence
37. You're The Best Thing (That's Ever Happened To Me)
38. You Are Wonderful
39. You've Done It Once
40. You Keep Changing Me
41. You Satisfy

Add 10% For S/H

D

THE WISDOM CENTER
P.O. Box 99, Denton, Texas 76202

1-888-WISDOM1
(1-888-947-3661)

Website:
WWW.THEWISDOMCENTER.TV

The Uncommon Woman

▸ **Master Keys In Understanding The Man In Your Life**

▸ **The One Thing Every Man Attempts To Move Away From**

▸ **The Dominant Difference Between A Wrong Woman And A Right Woman**

▸ **What Causes Men To Withdraw**

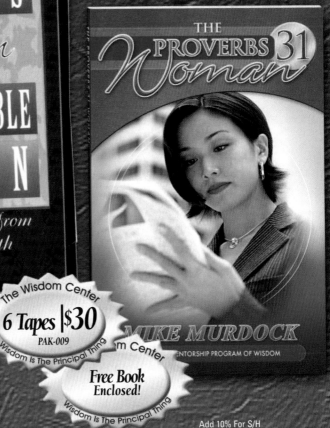

MIKE MURDOCK

THE WISDOM FOR WOMEN SERIES

THIRTY - ONE SECRETS of an **UNFORGETTABLE WOMAN**

Master Secrets from the life of Ruth

THE WISDOM CENTER
THE WISDOM CENTER
MIKE MURDOCK • P.O. Box 99 • Denton, Texas

31 Secrets of an Unforgettable Woman

The Wisdom Center
6 Tapes $30
PAK-009
Wisdom Is The Principal Thing

Free Book Enclosed!
Wisdom Is The Principal Thing

THE PROVERBS 31 Woman

MIKE MURDOCK
MENTORSHIP PROGRAM OF WISDOM

Add 10% For S/H

DISCOVER MasterCard VISA

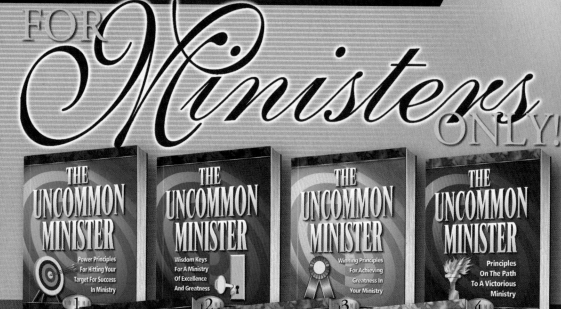
   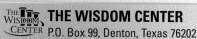

The Wisdom Center *Book Display* (72")

THE WISDOM CENTER BOOK DISPLAY CONTAINS 445 BOOKS!

Slot #	Item #	Title Of Books	Quantity	Retail Cost Per Book	Total Retail Value
1	B-01	Wisdom For Winning	5	$10.00 ea	$50.00
2	B-01	Wisdom For Winning	5	$10.00 ea	$50.00
3	B-11	Dream Seeds	12	$9.00 ea	$108.00
4	B-26	The God Book	7	$10.00 ea	$70.00
5	B-27	The Jesus Book	7	$10.00 ea	$70.00
6	B-28	The Blessing Bible	6	$10.00 ea	$60.00
7	B-29	The Survival Bible	6	$10.00 ea	$60.00
8	B-40	Wisdom For Crisis Times	9	$9.00 ea	$81.00
9	B-42	One-Minute Businessman's Devotional	5	$12.00 ea	$60.00
10	B-43	One-Minute Businesswoman's Devotional	5	$12.00 ea	$60.00
11	B-44	31 Secrets For Career Success	9	$10.00 ea	$90.00
12	B-45	101 Wisdom Keys	17	$5.00 ea	$85.00
13	B-46	31 Facts About Wisdom	15	$5.00 ea	$75.00
14	B-47	Covenant Of Fifty-Eight Blessings	10	$8.00 ea	$80.00
15	B-48	31 Keys To A New Beginning	15	$5.00 ea	$75.00
16	B-49	The Proverbs 31 Woman	13	$7.00 ea	$91.00
17	B-54	31 Greatest Chapters In The Bible	5	$10.00 ea	$50.00
18	B-57	31 Secrets Of An Unforgettable Woman	8	$9.00 ea	$72.00
19	B-71	Wisdom: God's Golden Key To Success	11	$7.00 ea	$77.00
20	B-72	Double Diamond Daily Devotional	3	$15.00 ea	$45.00
21	B-74	The Assignment Vol. 1: The Dream And The Destiny	8	$10.00 ea	$80.00
22	B-75	The Assignment Vol. 2: The Anointing And The Adversity	7	$10.00 ea	$70.00
23	B-82	31 Reasons People Do Not Receive Their Financial Harvest	5	$12.00 ea	$60.00
24	B-82	31 Reasons People Do Not Receive Their Financial Harvest	5	$12.00 ea	$60.00
25	B-91	The Leadership Secrets Of Jesus	6	$10.00 ea	$60.00
26	B-91	The Leadership Secrets Of Jesus	6	$10.00 ea	$60.00
27	B-92	Secrets Of Journey Vol. 1	15	$5.00 ea	$75.00
28	B-93	Secrets Of Journey Vol. 2	15	$5.00 ea	$75.00
29	B-97	The Assignment Vol. 3: The Trials And The Triumph	7	$10.00 ea	$70.00
30	B-98	The Assignment Vol. 4: The Pain And The Passion	7	$10.00 ea	$70.00
31	B-99	Secrets Of The Richest Man Who Ever Lived	6	$10.00 ea	$60.00
32	B-99	Secrets Of The Richest Man Who Ever Lived	6	$10.00 ea	$60.00
33	B-100	Holy Spirit Handbook Vol. 1	8	$10.00 ea	$80.00
34	B-101	The 3 Most Important Things In Your Life	5	$10.00 ea	$50.00
35	B-101	The 3 Most Important Things In Your Life	5	$10.00 ea	$50.00
36	B-104	7 Keys To 1000 Times More	8	$10.00 ea	$80.00
37	B-104	7 Keys To 1000 Times More	8	$10.00 ea	$80.00
38	B-107	The Uncommon Minister Vol. 1	15	$5.00 ea	$75.00
39	B-108	The Uncommon Minister Vol. 2	15	$5.00 ea	$75.00
40	B-114	The Law Of Recognition	5	$10.00 ea	$50.00
41	B-114	The Law Of Recognition	5	$10.00 ea	$50.00
42	B-115	Seeds Of Wisdom On The Secret Place	15	$5.00 ea	$75.00
43	B-116	Seeds Of Wisdom On The Holy Spirit	15	$5.00 ea	$75.00
44	B-117	Seeds Of Wisdom On The Word Of God	15	$5.00 ea	$75.00
45	B-118	Seeds Of Wisdom On Problem Solving	15	$5.00 ea	$75.00
46	B-122	Seeds Of Wisdom On Your Assignment	15	$5.00 ea	$75.00
47	B-127	Seeds Of Wisdom On Goal-Setting	15	$5.00 ea	$75.00
48	B-137	Seeds Of Wisdom On Productivity	15	$5.00 ea	$75.00

Total of 445 Books and Display ~~$3,674.00~~

$1,985.00

 THE WISDOM CENTER
P.O. Box 99, Denton, Texas 76202

1-888-WISDOM1
(1-888-947-3661)

 Website:
WWW.THEWISDOMCENTER.TV

I

GIFTS OF WISDOM...

SPECIALTY *Bibles*

*Each Book Sold Separately

- ▶ **The Businessman's Topical Bible** (B-33 / $10)
- ▶ **The Children's Topical Bible** (B-154 / $10)
- ▶ **The Father's Topical Bible** (B-35 / $10)
- ▶ **The Grandparent's Topical Bible** (B-34 / $10)
- ▶ **The Minister's Topical Bible** (B-32 / $10)
- ▶ **The Mother's Topical Bible** (B-36 / $10)
- ▶ **The New Believer's Topical Bible** (B-37 / $10)
- ▶ **The Seeds of Wisdom Topical Bible** (B-31 / $10)
- ▶ **The ServiceMan's Topical Bible** (B-138 / $10)

- ▶ **The Teen's Topical Bible** (B-30 / $10)
- ▶ **The Traveler's Topical Bible** (B-139 / $10)
- ▶ **The Widow's Topical Bible** (B-38 / $10)

The Wisdom Center

Only $10

Wisdom Is The Principal Thing

Add 10% For S/H

J **THE WISDOM CENTER** P.O. Box 99, Denton, Texas 76202

1-888-WISDOM1
(1-888-947-3661)

Website: ─────
WWW.THEWISDOMCENTER.TV

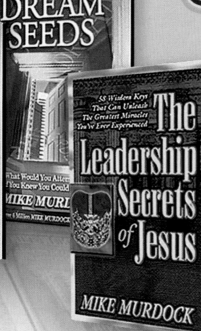

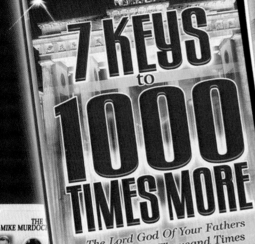

The Wisdom Journal

"Write The Things
Which Thou Hast
Seen, And The
Things Which Are,
And The Things
Which Shall Be
Hereafter."

-Revelation 1:19

MY WISDOM JOURNAL

My Wisdom Journal

Stunningly beautiful Black and Gold
Leatherette. Contains 160 pages for
your personal journalizing and
diary...a different Wisdom Key for
each day...it also includes:

► 101 Wisdom Keys
► 31 Facts About Favor
► 31 Facts About Wisdom
► 31 Facts About The Holy Spirit
► 31 Qualities Of An Unforgettable Woman
► 58 Leadership Secrets Of Jesus
► Read The Bible Through In A Year Program
► Sample Page For Effective Note Taking

The Wisdom Center

$20 Each

B-163

Wisdom Is The Principal Thing

Add 10% For S/H

N THE WISDOM CENTER
P.O. Box 99, Denton, Texas 76202

1-888-WISDOM1
(1-888-947-3661)

Website:
WWW.THEWISDOMCENTER.TV

JOIN THE
Wisdom Key 3000
TODAY!

Dear Partner,

God has connected us!

I have asked the Holy Spirit for 3000 Special Partners who will plant a monthly Seed of $58.00 to help me bring the gospel around the world. (58 represents 58 kinds of blessing in the Bible.)

Will you become my monthly Faith Partner in The Wisdom Key 3000? Your monthly Seed of $58.00 is so powerful in helping heal broken lives. When you sow into the work of God, 4 Miracle Harvests are guaranteed in Scripture:

- ► Uncommon Protection (Mal. 3:10,11)
- ► Uncommon Favor (Lk. 6:38)
- ► Uncommon Health (Isa. 58:8)
- ► Financial Ideas and Wisdom (Deut. 8:18)

Your Faith Partner,

Mike Murdock

□ **Yes Mike, I want to join The Wisdom Key 3000. Enclosed is my monthly Seed-Faith Promise of □ $58 □ Other $_____. Please rush The Wisdom Key Partnership Pak to me today!**

□CHECK □MONEY ORDER □AMEX □DISCOVER □MASTERCARD □VISA

Credit Card # _____ Exp. ____/____

Signature _____

Name _____ Birth Date ____/____/____

Address _____

City _____ State _____ Zip _____

Phone _____ E-Mail _____

Your Seed-Faith offerings are used to support the Mike Murdock Evangelistic Association, The Wisdom Center and all its programs. The Ministry reserves the right to redirect funds as needed in order to carry out our charitable purpose.

Clip and mail completed form to:

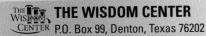 **THE WISDOM CENTER** P.O. Box 99, Denton, Texas 76202

1-888-WISDOM1 (1-888-947-3661)

Website: WWW.THEWISDOMCENTER.TV

O

THE WISDOM COMMEN[TARY]

Wisdom Determines Your Wealth.

Wisdom Determines Your Favor.

Wisdom Determines Your Health.

Wisdom Determines Your Success.

Wisdom Is The Golden Gate
To Greatness.

Wisdom Is The Mysterious Magnet
For Miracles.

Wisdom Is The Unseen Persuader
In Successful Negotiations.

Wisdom Is The Unstoppable
Weapon Of Every Winning
Warrior.

Wisdom Is The Master Secret Of
Every Successful Marriage.

Wisdom Is The Only Weapon
Needed To Win Any War.

Wisdom Is The Only Bridge From
Poverty To Prosperity.

Wisdom Is Simply The Law Of
God...Applied Accurately To Solve
A Problem.

Wisdom Is Using The Scriptural
Solution To Solve Any Problem.

Ignorance Is The Only True Enemy
Capable Of Destroying You.

DR. MIKE MURDOCK is in tremendous demand as one of the most dynamic speakers in America today. More than 14,000 audiences in 38 countries have attended his Schools of Wisdom. Hundreds of invitations come to him from churches, colleges, and business corporations. He is a noted author of over 130 books, including the best sellers, "The Leadership Secrets of Jesus" and "Secrets of the Richest Man Who Ever Lived." Thousands view his weekly television program, "Wisdom Keys with Mike Murdock." Many attend his Saturday School of Wisdom Breakfasts that he hosts in major cities of America. His headquarters, The Wisdom Center, is located in Denton, Texas.

THE
WISDOM
CENTER

P.O. Box 99
Denton, Texas 76202
1.888.WISDOM1
1.888.947.3661

PHONE FOR FREE CATALOG!

WEBSITE: WWW.THEWISDOMCENTER.TV